GREAT PIANO SOLOS

THE TV BOOK

Wise Publications
part of The Music Sales Group

London/New York/Paris/Sydney/Copenhagen/Berlin/Madrid/Tokyo

Published by
Wise Publications
8/9 Frith Street, London W1D 3JB, UK.

Exclusive Distributors:
Music Sales Limited
Distribution Centre, Newmarket Road,
Bury St Edmunds, Suffolk IP33 3YB, UK.

Music Sales Pty Limited
120 Rothschild Avenue,
Rosebery, NSW 2018, Australia.

Order No. AM985479
ISBN 1-84609-524-7
This book © Copyright 2006 by Wise Publications
a division of Music Sales Limited.

Printed in the EU.

Your Guarantee of Quality:
As publishers, we strive to produce every book to the highest commercial
standards. This book has been carefully designed to minimise awkward
page turns and to make playing from it a real pleasure. Particular care has
been given to specifying acid-free, neutral-sized paper made from pulps
which have not been elemental chlorine bleached. This pulp is from farmed
sustainable forests and was produced with special regard for the
environment. Throughout, the printing and binding have been planned to
ensure a sturdy, attractive publication which should give years of
enjoyment. If your copy fails to meet our high standards, please inform us
and we will gladly replace it.

www.musicsales.com

CONTENTS

The 'A' Team

Music by Mike Post & Pete Carpenter

Mercenary, sempre con tutta forza

Agatha Christie's Poirot

Words & Music by Christopher Gunning

The Avengers

Music by Laurie Johnson

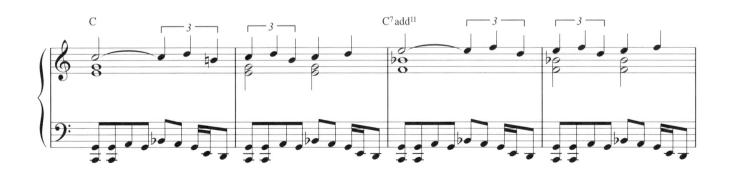

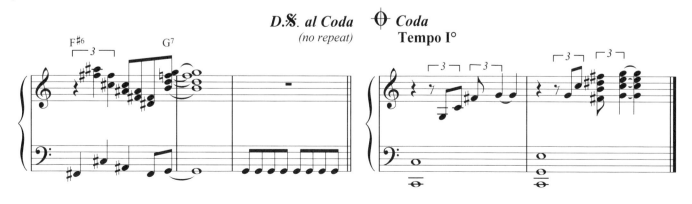

Blackadder

Music by Howard Goodall

15

Bleak House

Music by Geoffrey Burgon

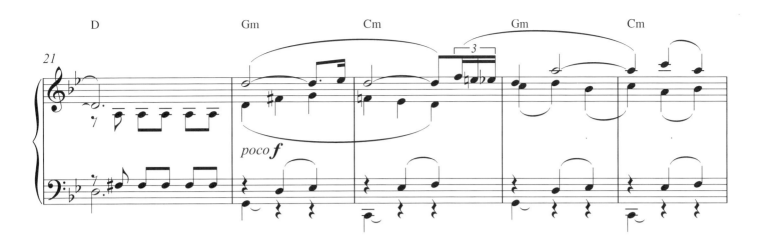

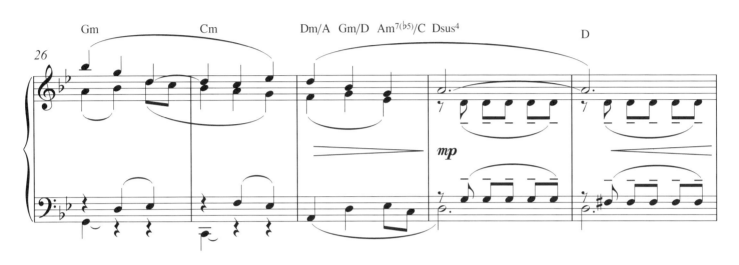

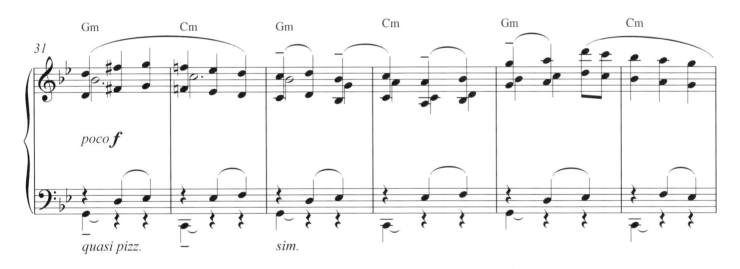

poco rit. al fine

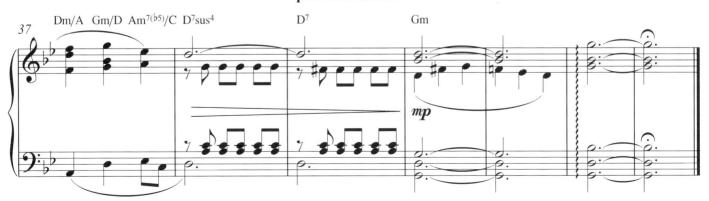

Brideshead Revisited

Music by Geoffrey Burgon

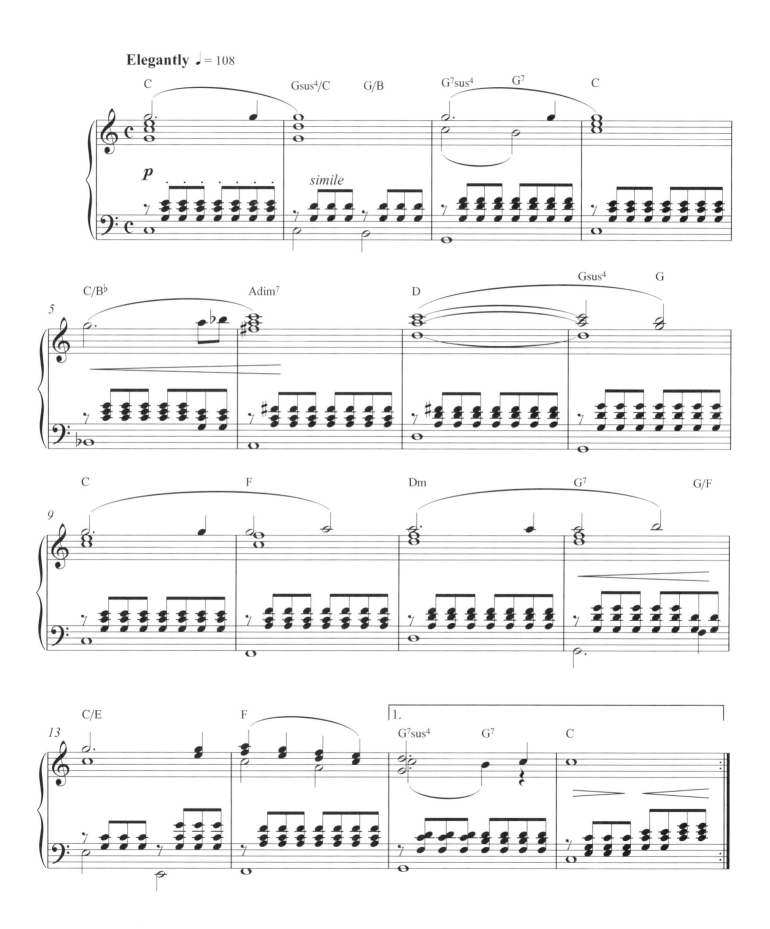

Cagney And Lacey

Music by Bill Conti

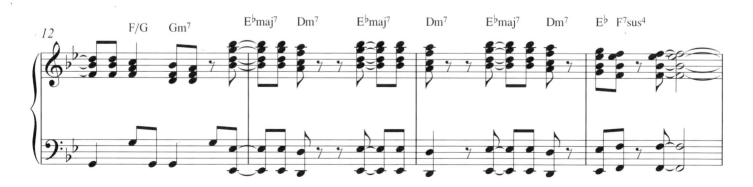

Casualty

Music by Kenneth Freeman

Urgent and rhythmic ♩ = 146

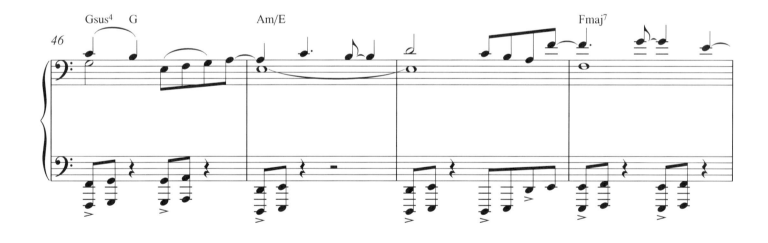

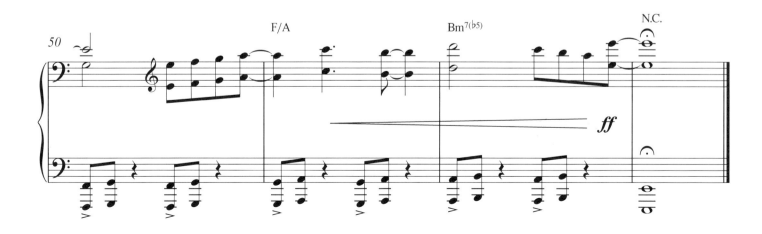

Columbo

Music by Billy Goldenberg

31

Cheers

Where Everybody Knows Your Name

Words by Judy Hunt Angelo
Music by Gary Portnoy

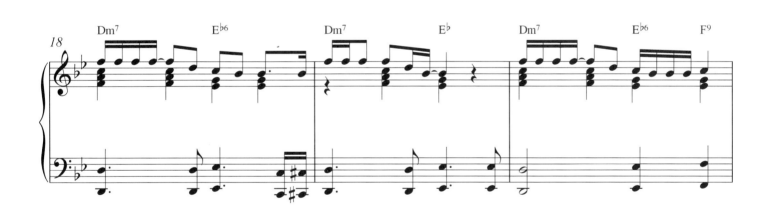

Crossroads

Music by Tony Hatch

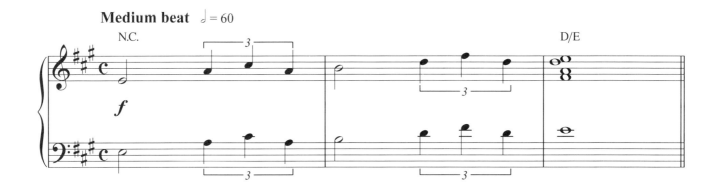

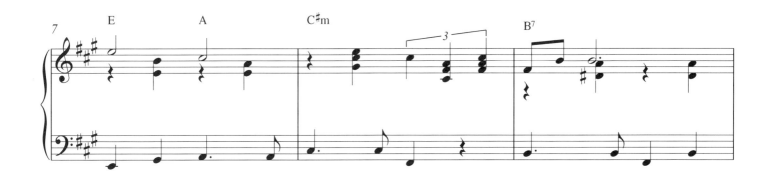

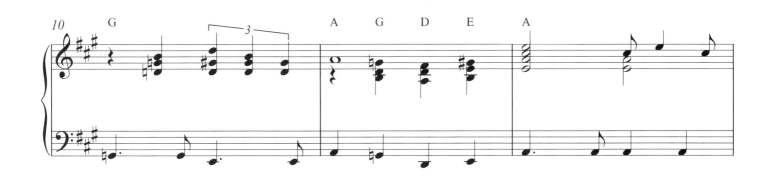

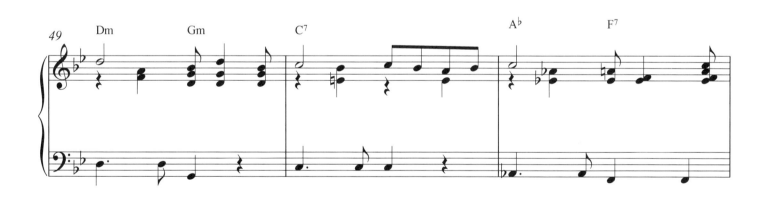

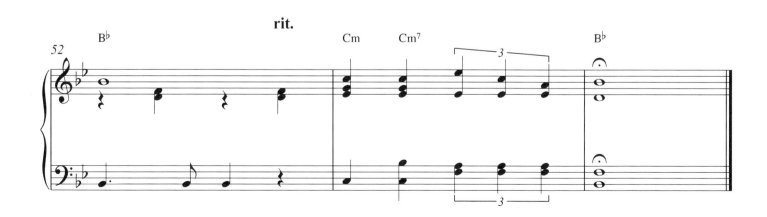

Dragnet

Words & Music by David Newman

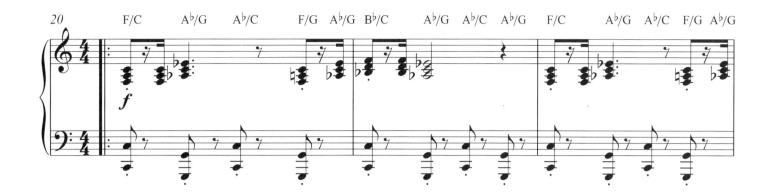

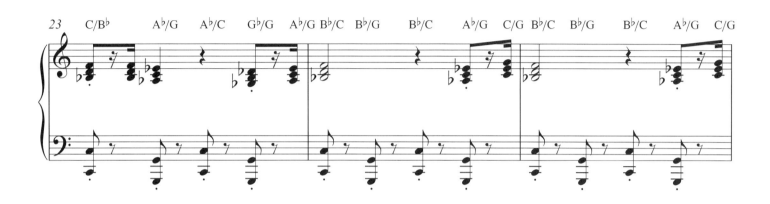

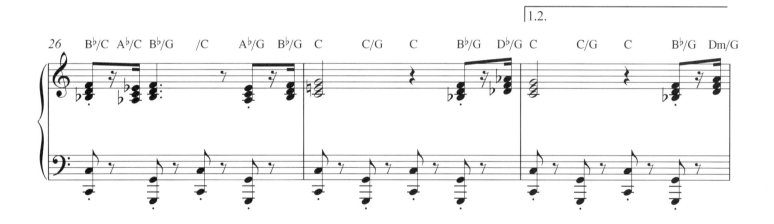

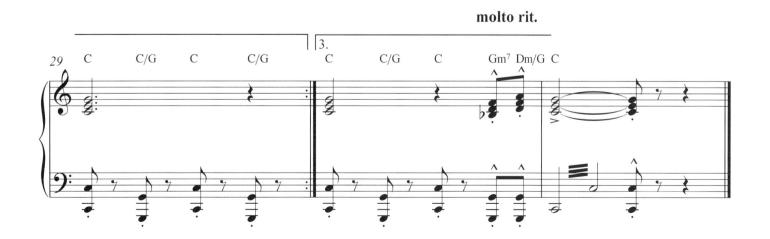

Dad's Army

Who Do You Think You Are Kidding Mr. Hitler?

Words by Jimmy Perry

Music by Jimmy Perry and Derek Taverner

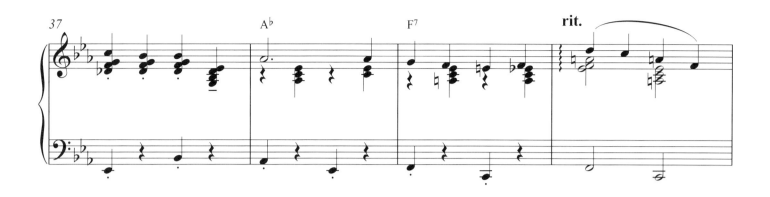

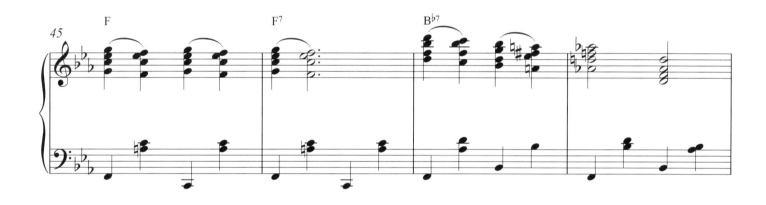

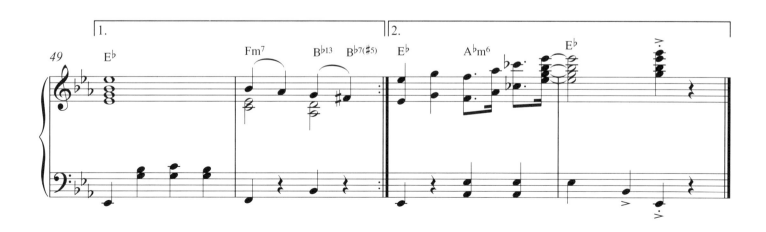

EastEnders

Music by Leslie Osborne & Simon May

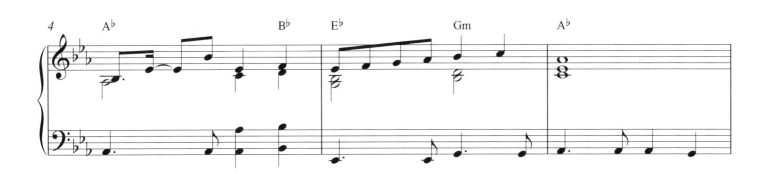

Fawlty Towers

Music by Dennis Wilson

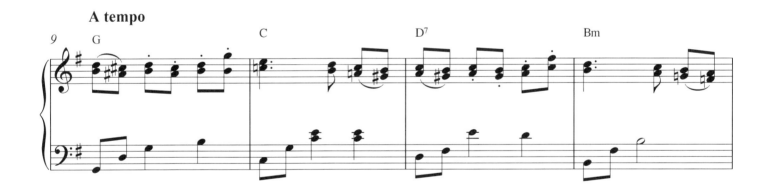

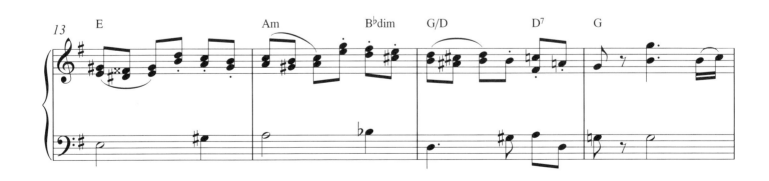

49

50

51

The Forsyte Saga

Irene's Song

Words & Music by Geoffrey Burgon

Moderate waltz (♩ = c. 120)

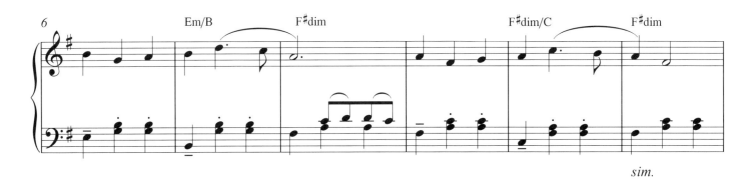

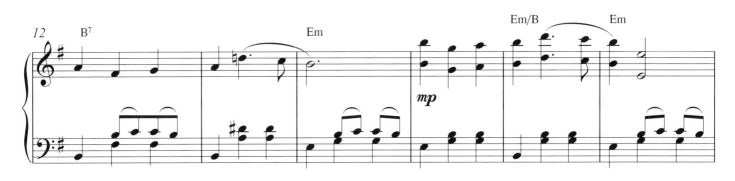

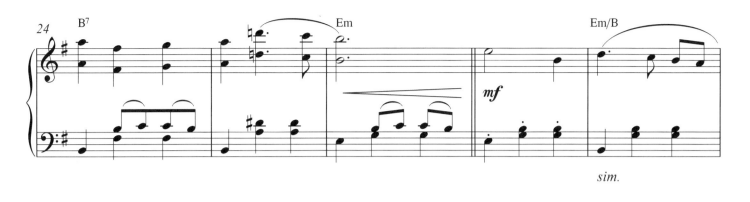

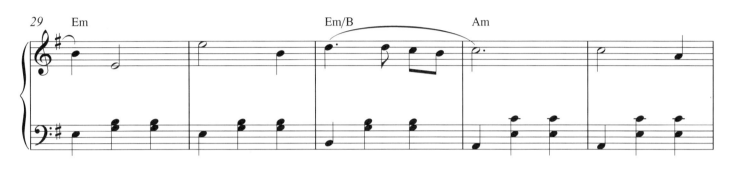

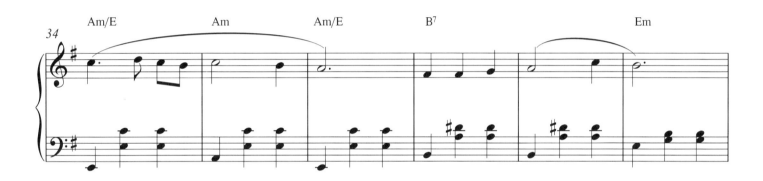

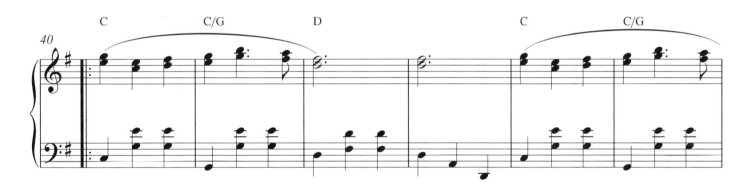

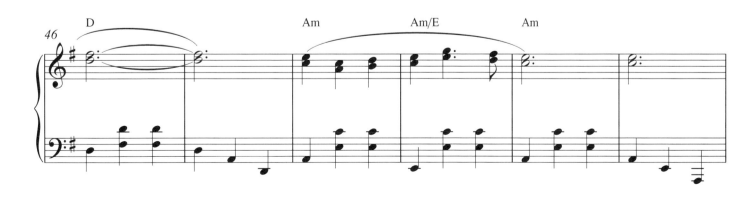

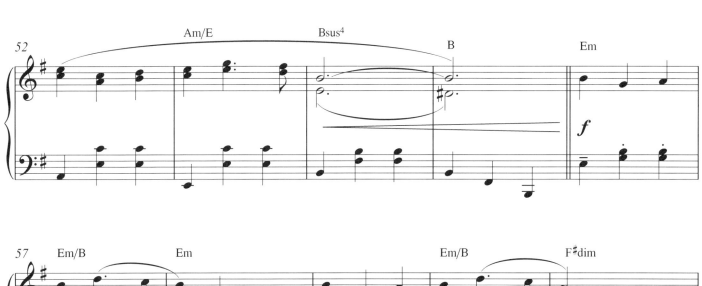

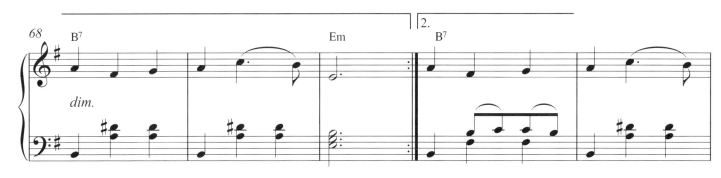

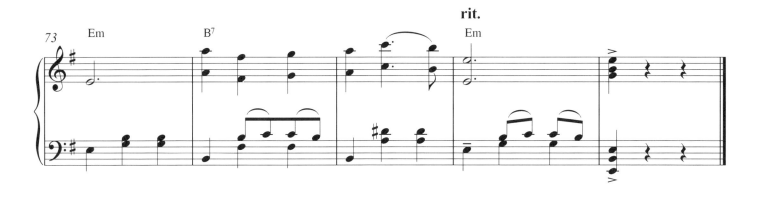

Frasier
Tossed Salad And Scrambled Eggs

Words & Music by Bruce Miller & Darryl Phinnessee

Goodnight Sweetheart

Words & Music by Calvin Carter & James Hudson

Happy Days

Words by Norman Gimbel
Music by Charles Fox

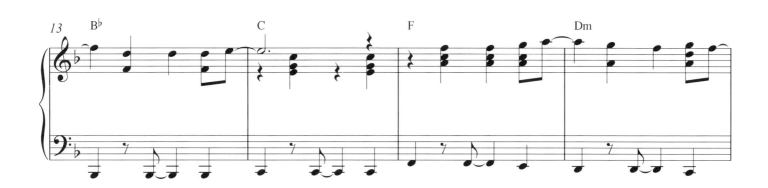

Heartbeat

Words & Music by Bob Montgomery & Norman Petty

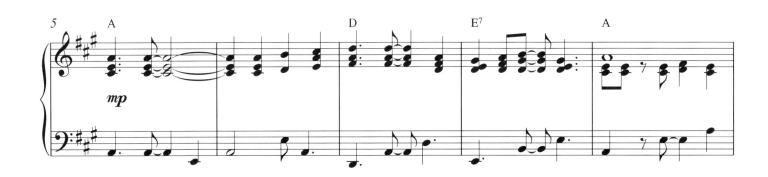

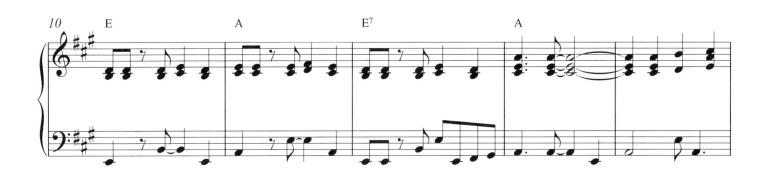

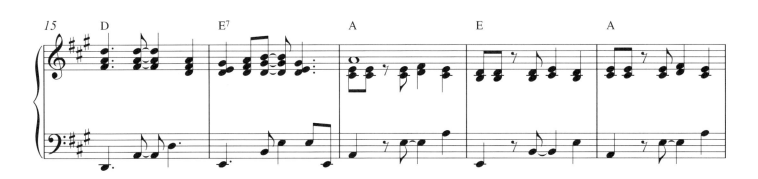

Jeeves And Wooster

Music by Anne Dudley

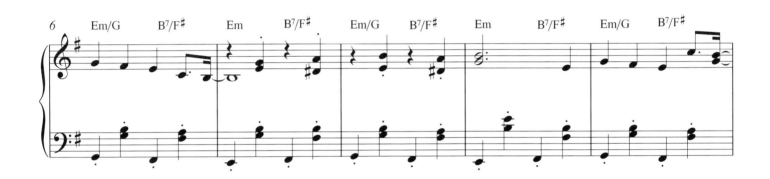

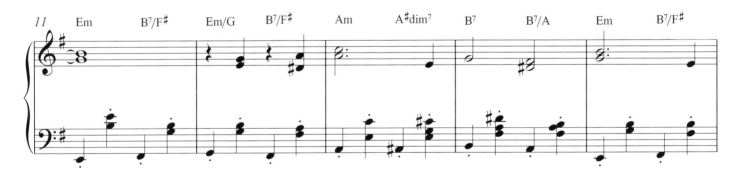

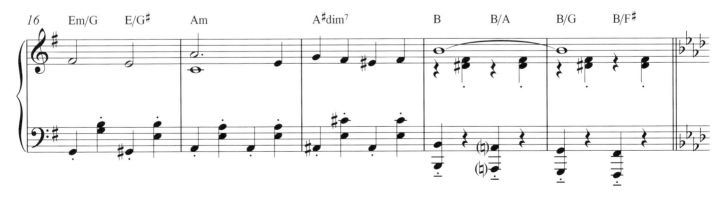

Kojak

Music by Billy Goldenberg

Maigret

Music by Nigel Hess

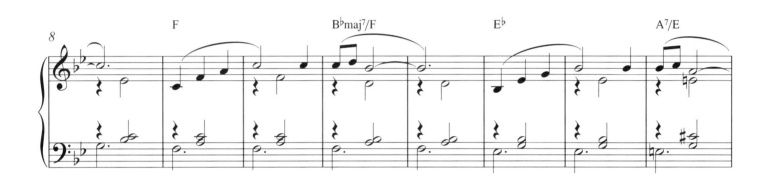

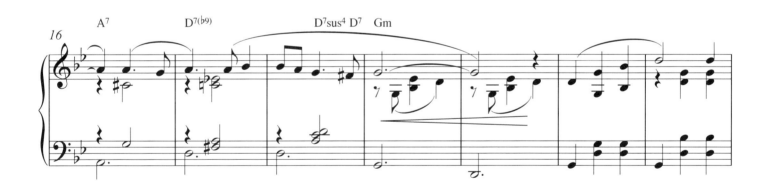

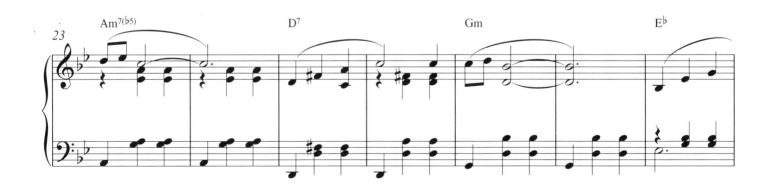

Mission: Impossible

Music by Lalo Schifrin

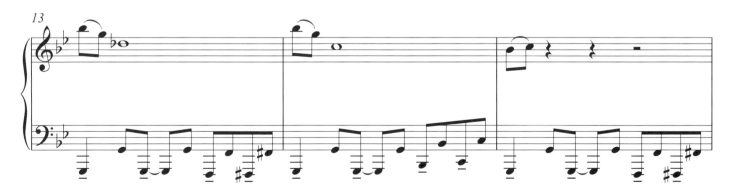

Miss Marple

Words & Music by Ken Howard & Alan Blaikley

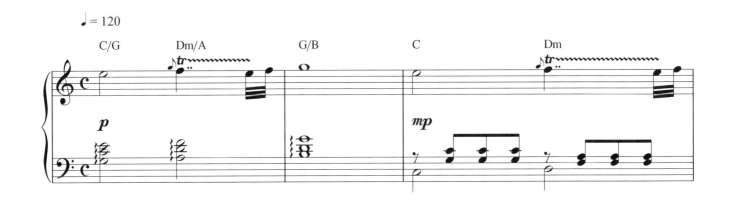

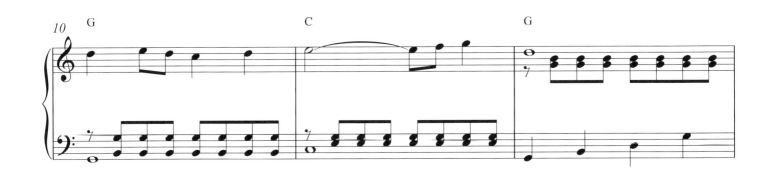

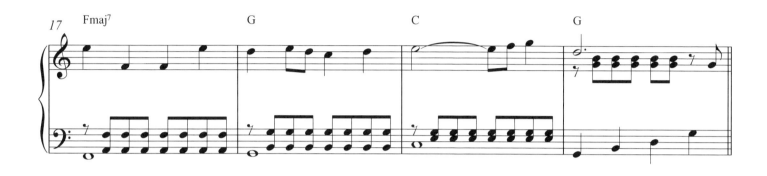

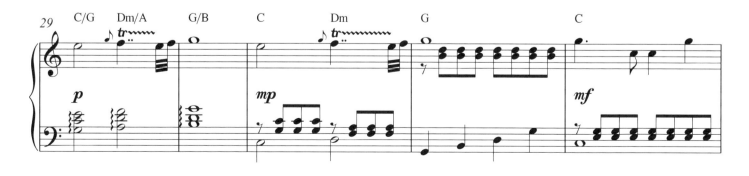

Moonlighting

Words by Al Jarreau

Music by Lee Holdridge

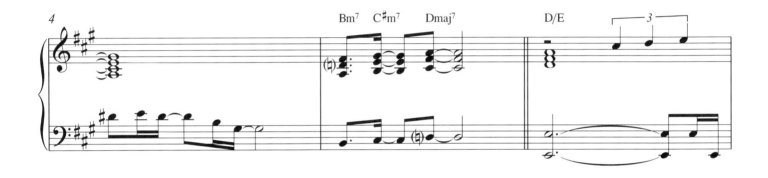

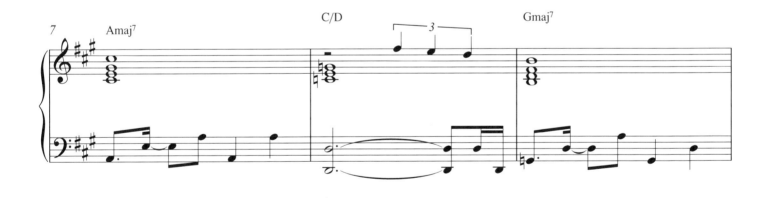

The Munsters

Music by Jack Marshall

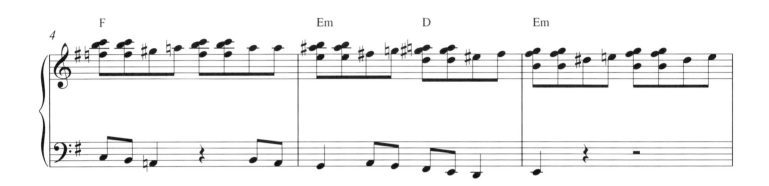

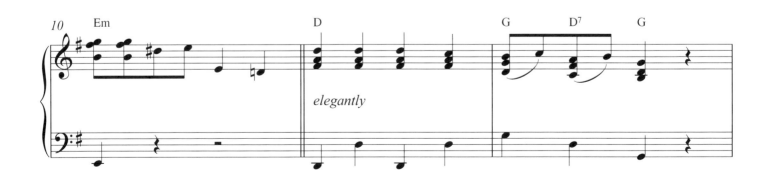

85

The Muppet Show

Music by Jim Henson & Sam Pottle

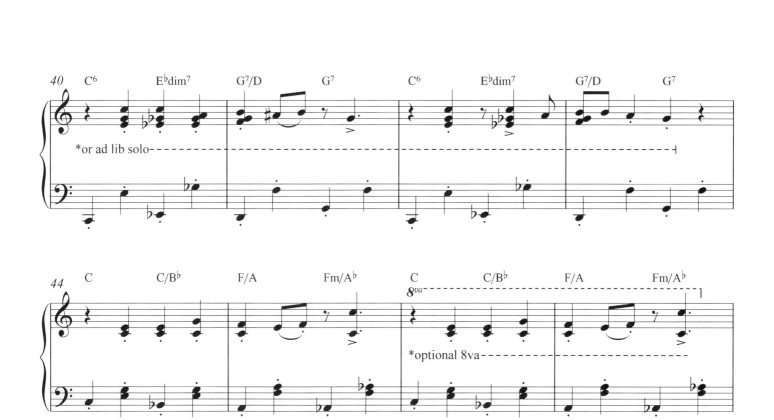

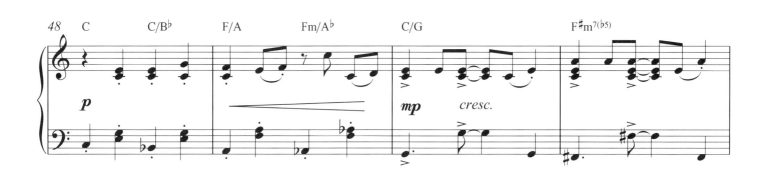

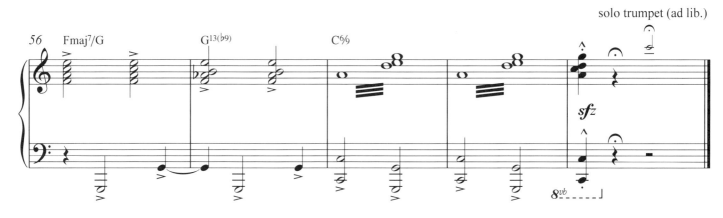

Murder She Wrote

Music by John Addison

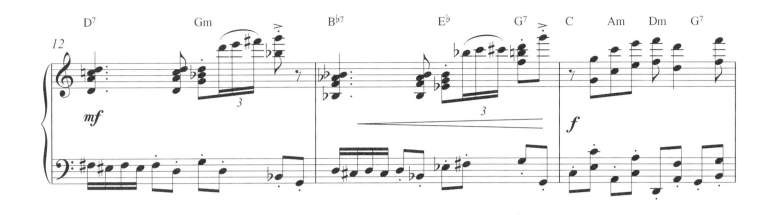

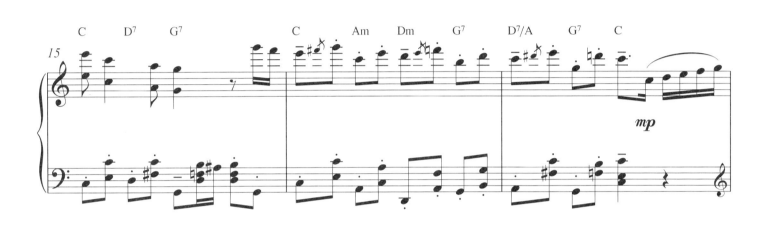

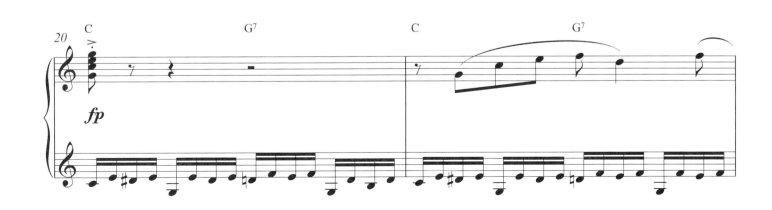

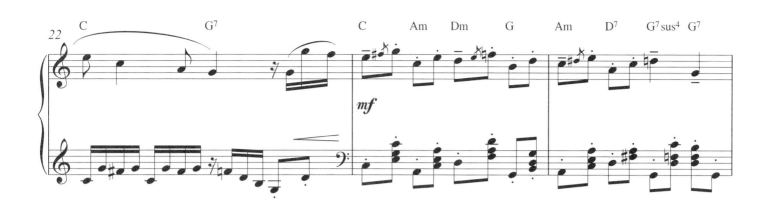

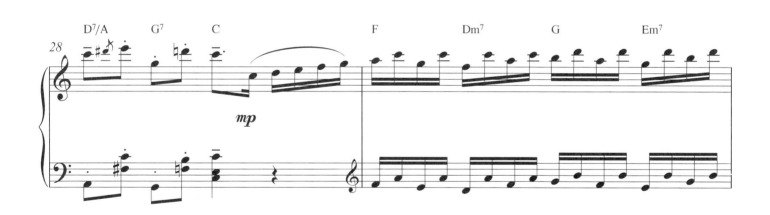

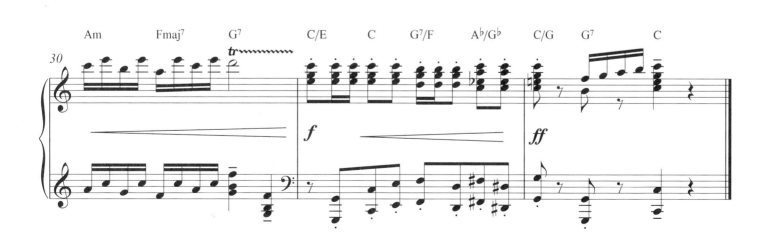

Neighbours

Words & Music by Tony Hatch & Jackie Trent

The Odd Couple

Music by Neal Hefti

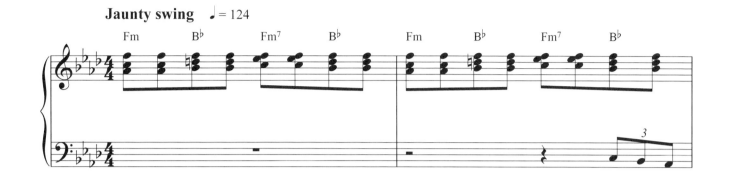

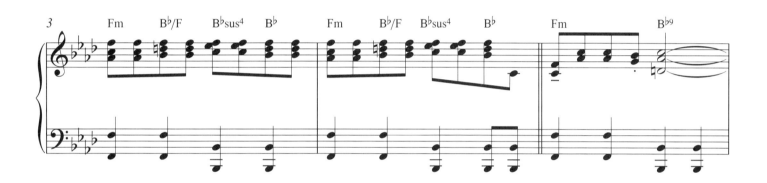

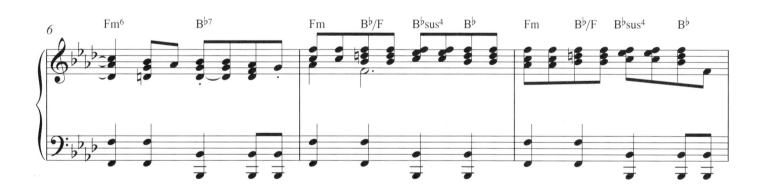

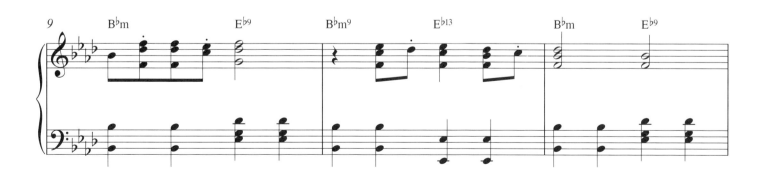

One Foot In The Grave

Words & Music by Eric Idle

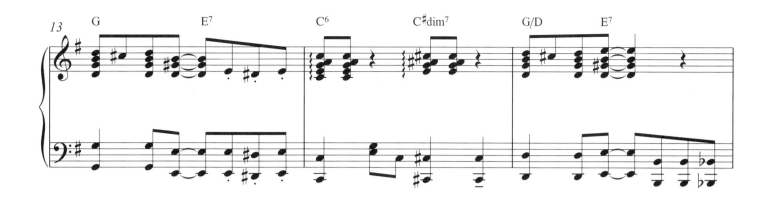

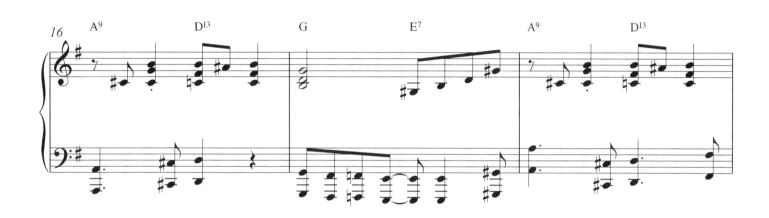

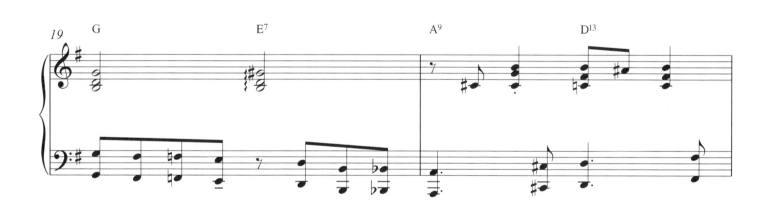

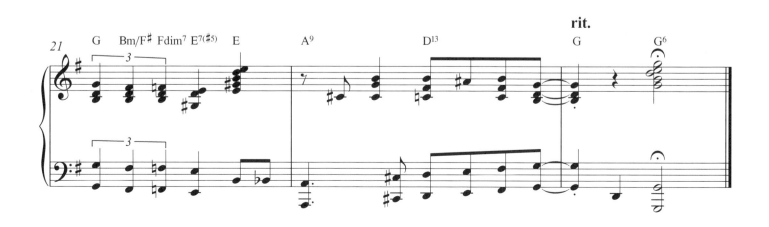

The Good Life

Music by Burt Rhodes

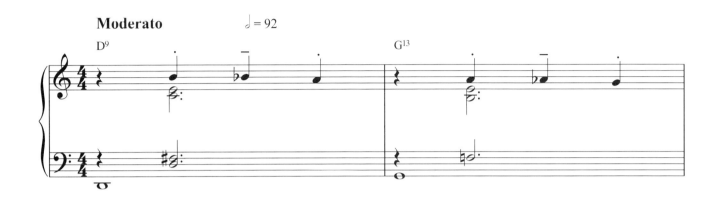

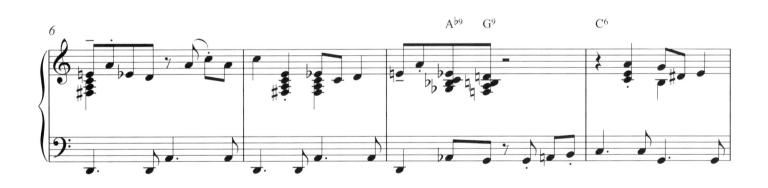

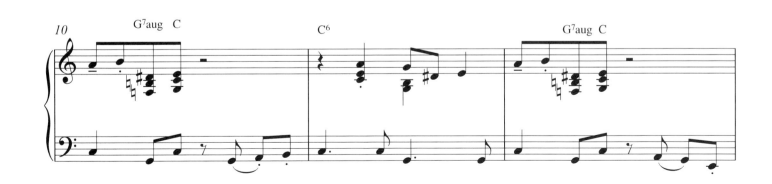

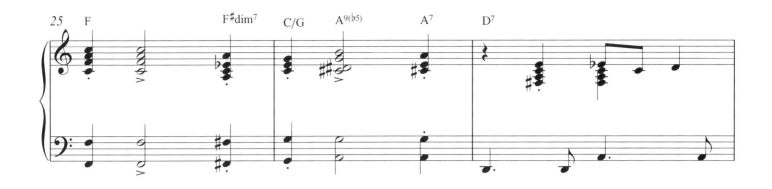

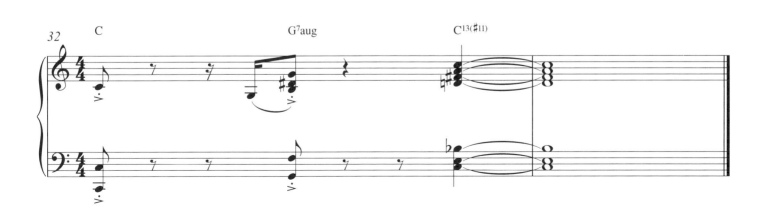

Only Fools And Horses

Opening Theme

Words & Music by John R. Sullivan

Only Fools And Horses
Closing Theme

Music by John R. Sullivan

The Professionals

Music by Laurie Johnson

The Royle Family

Half The World Away

Words & Music by Noel Gallagher

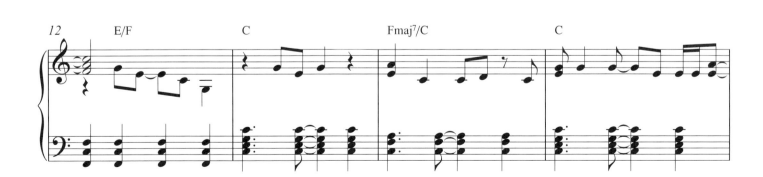

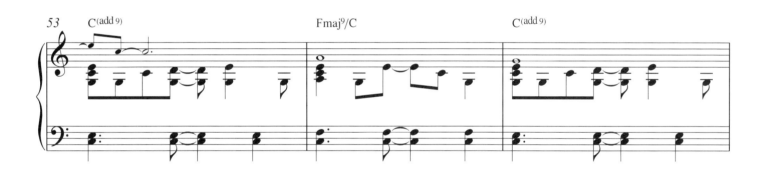

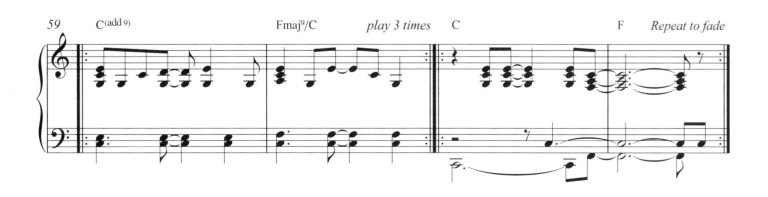

Sex And The City

Music by Thomas Findlay, Andrew Cocup & Douglas Cuomo

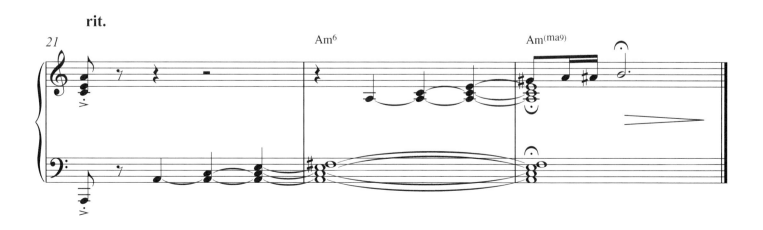

The Persuaders

Music by John Barry

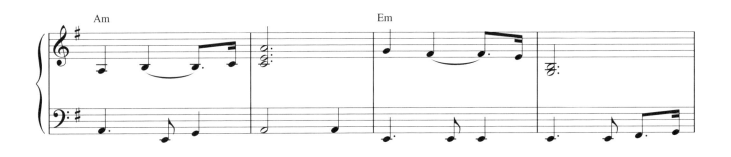

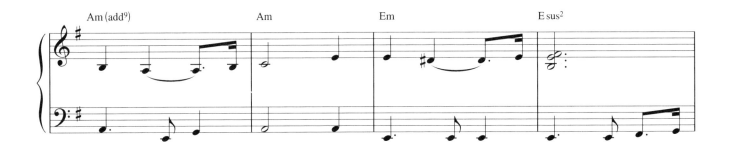

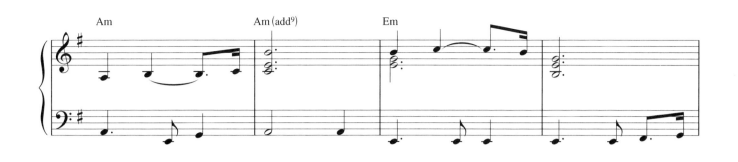

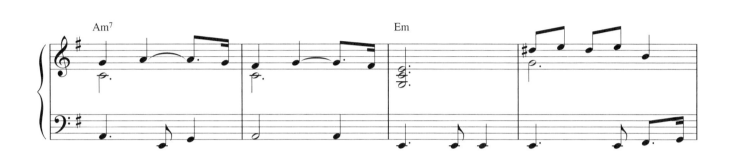

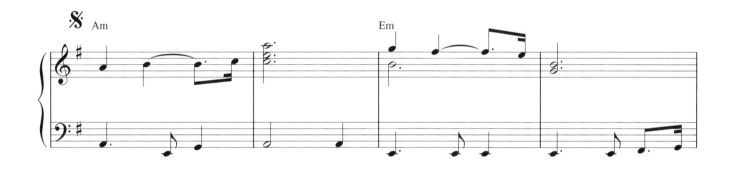

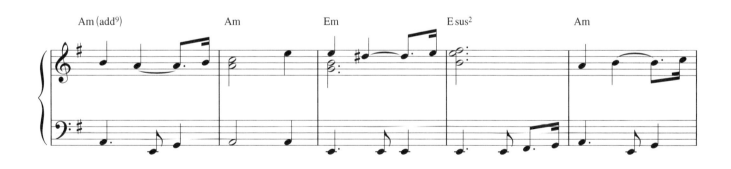

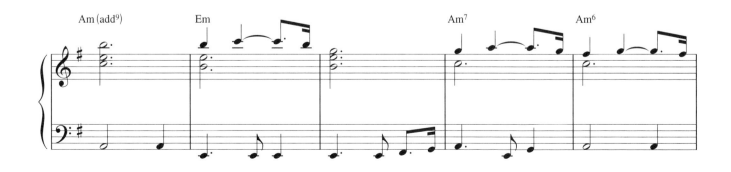

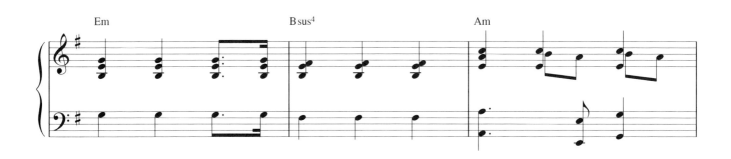

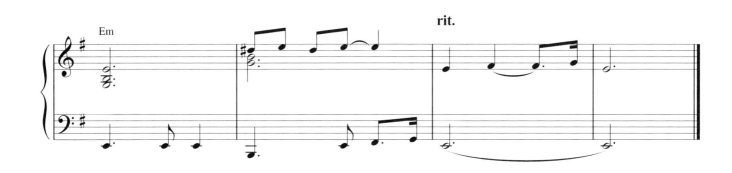

Ski Sunday

Pop Looks Bach

Music by Sam Fonteyn

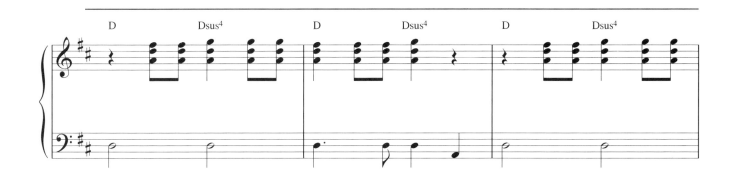

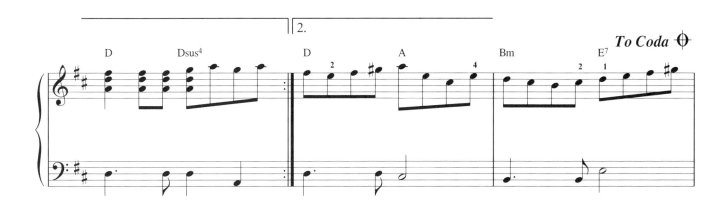

To Coda ⊕

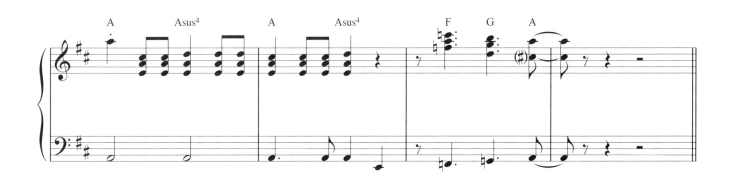

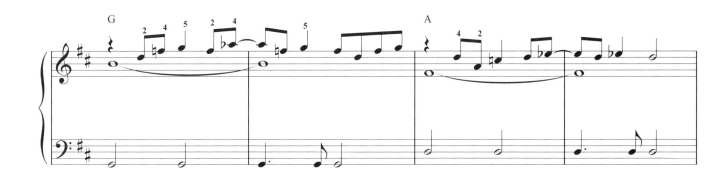

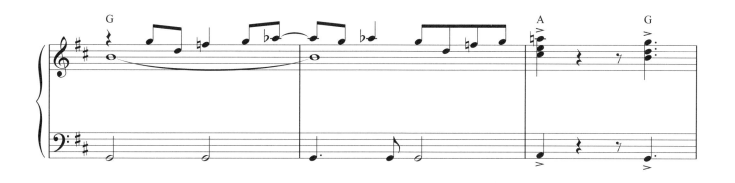

D.%. al Coda

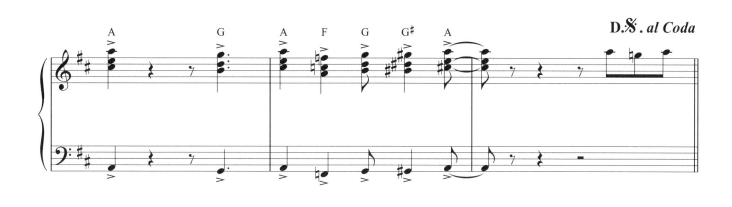

Coda

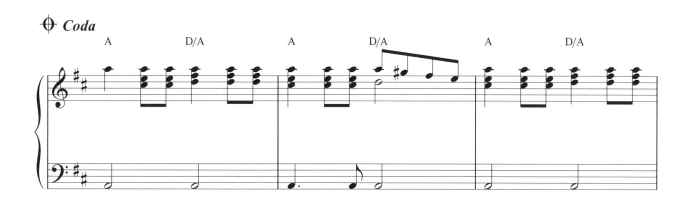

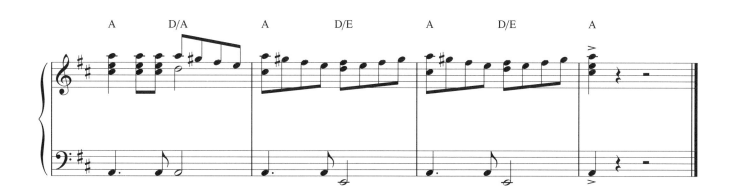

Six Feet Under

Music by Thomas Newman

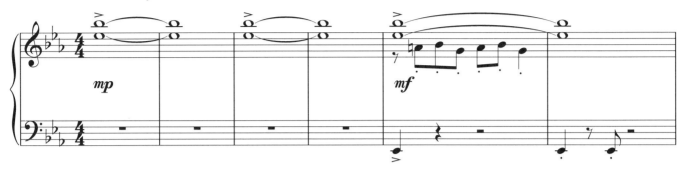

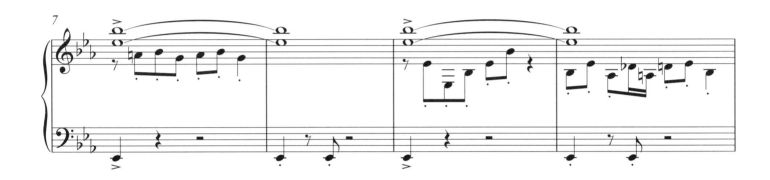

123

Shameless

Words & Music by Murray Gold

Steptoe And Son

Old Ned

Music by Ron Grainer

131

The Sweeney

Music by Harry South

Moderate swing ♩ = 120

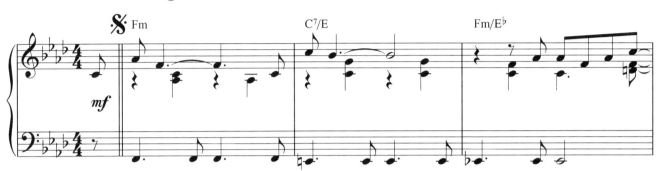

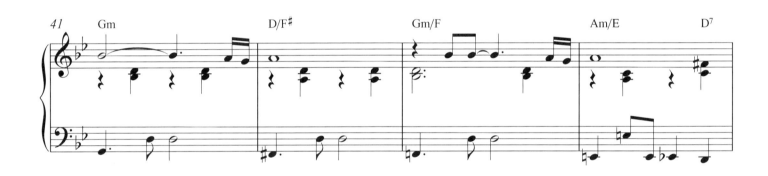

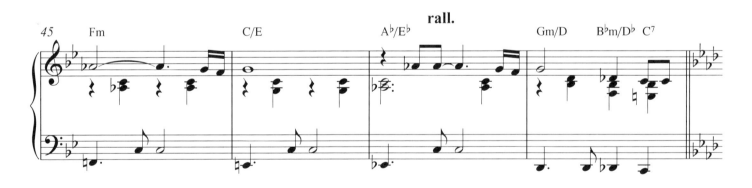

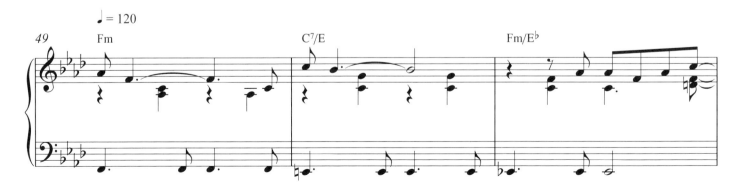

135

Tales Of The Unexpected

Music by Ron Grainer

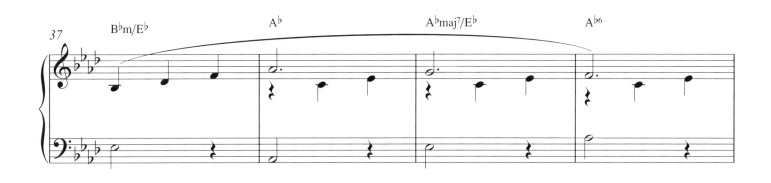

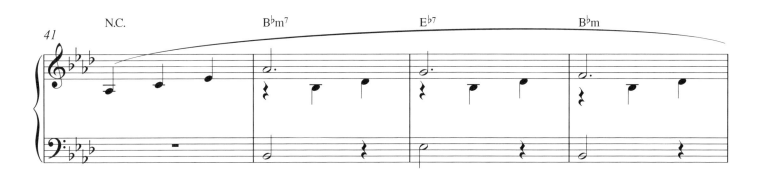

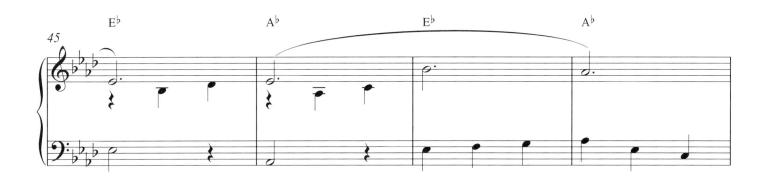

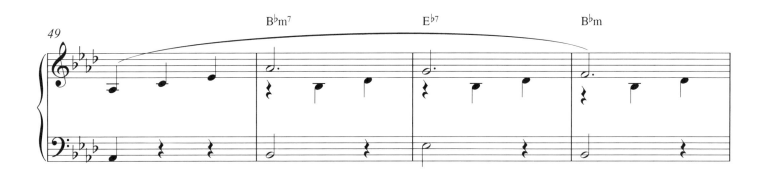

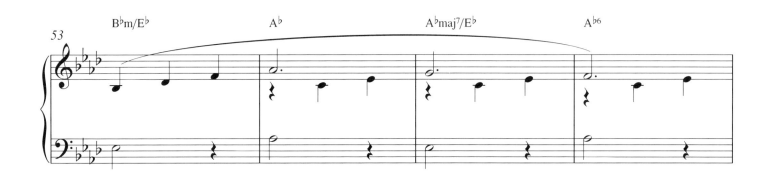

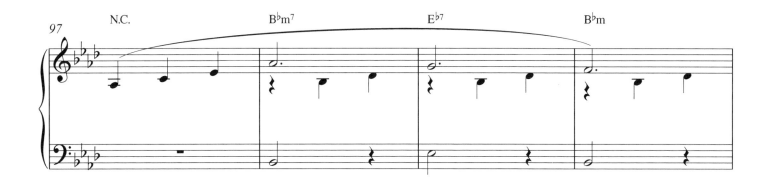
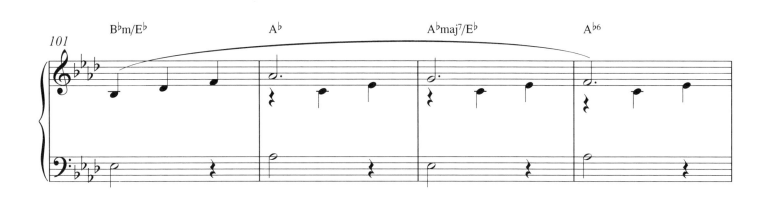
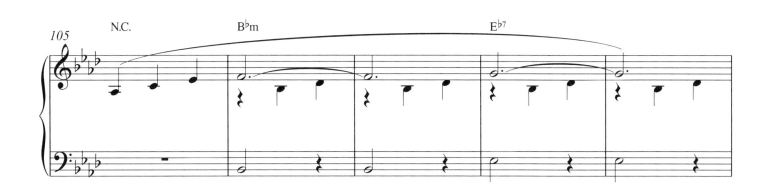
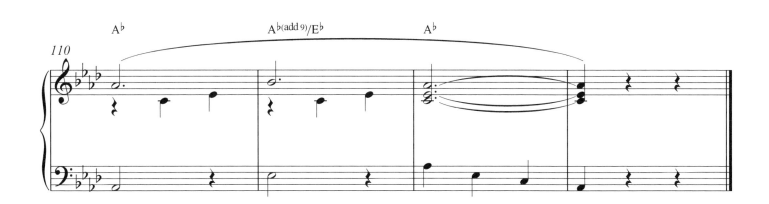

Taxi

'Angela'

Music by Bob James

Thunderbirds

Music by Barry Gray

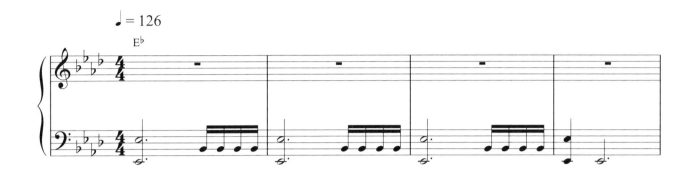

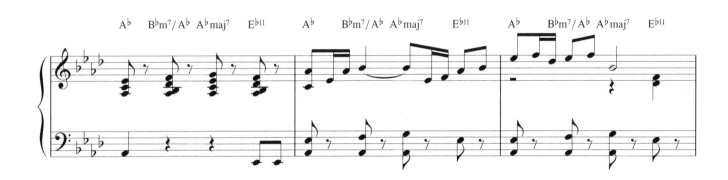

145

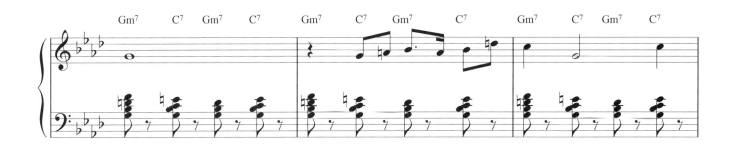

146

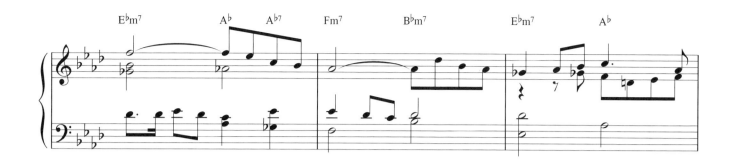

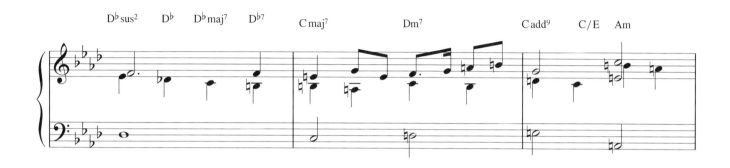

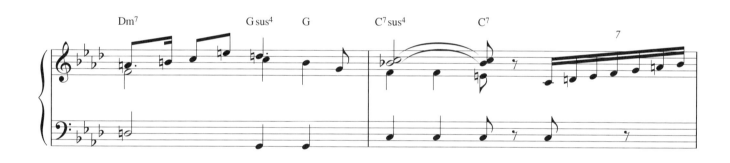

D.$.al Coda

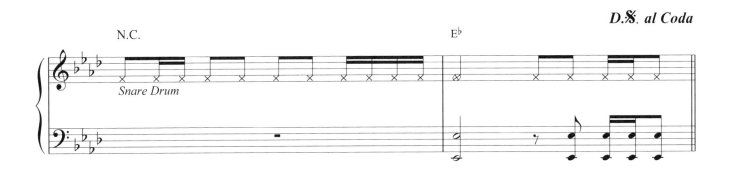

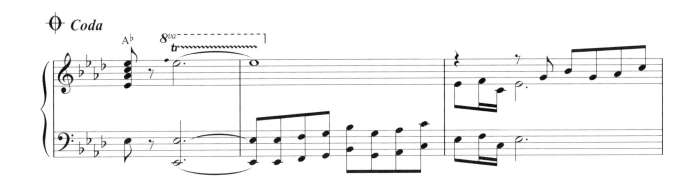

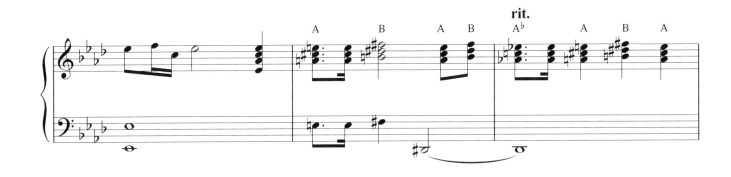

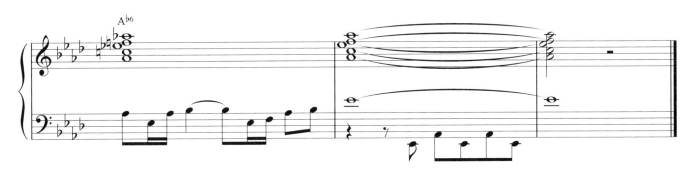

T.F.I. Friday

Man In A Suitcase

Words & Music by Sting

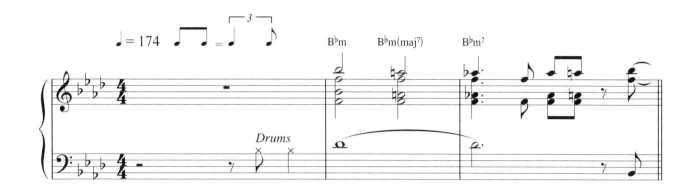

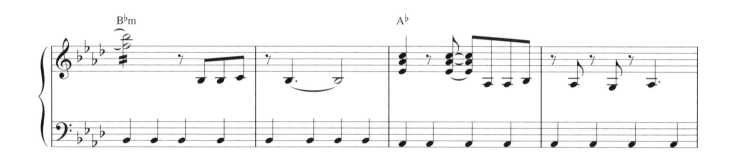

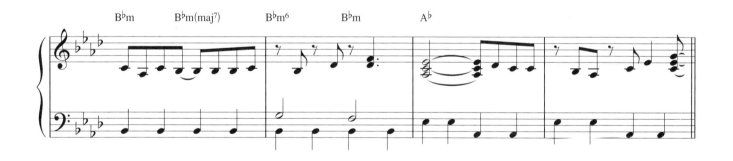

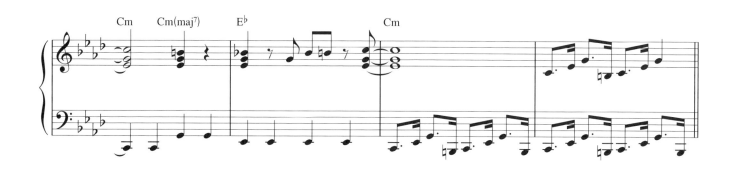

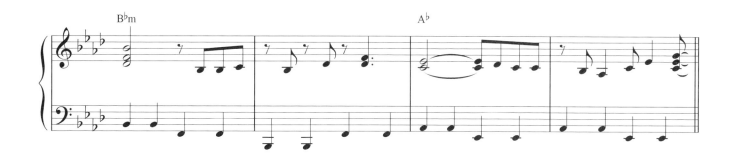

Twin Peaks

Music by Angelo Badalamenti & David Lynch

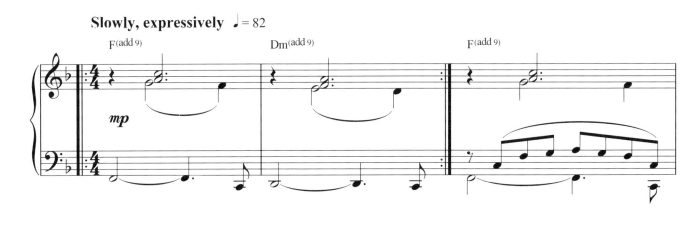

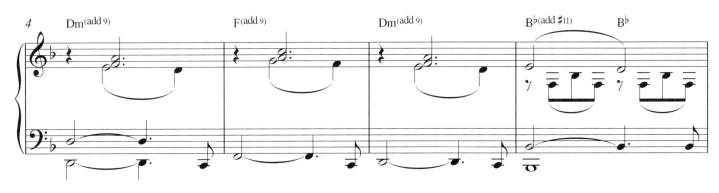

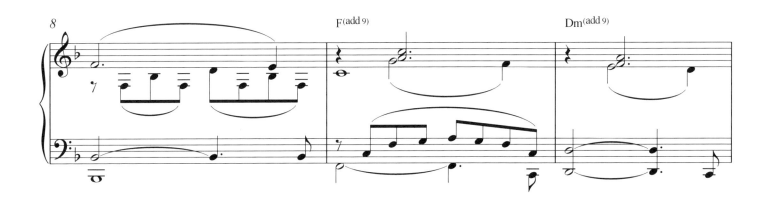

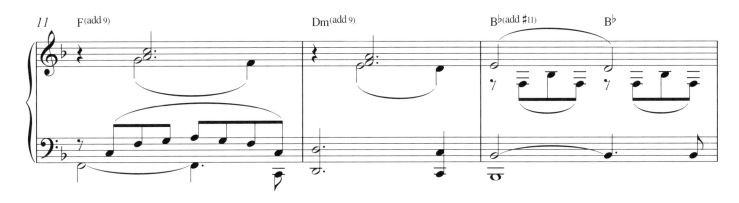

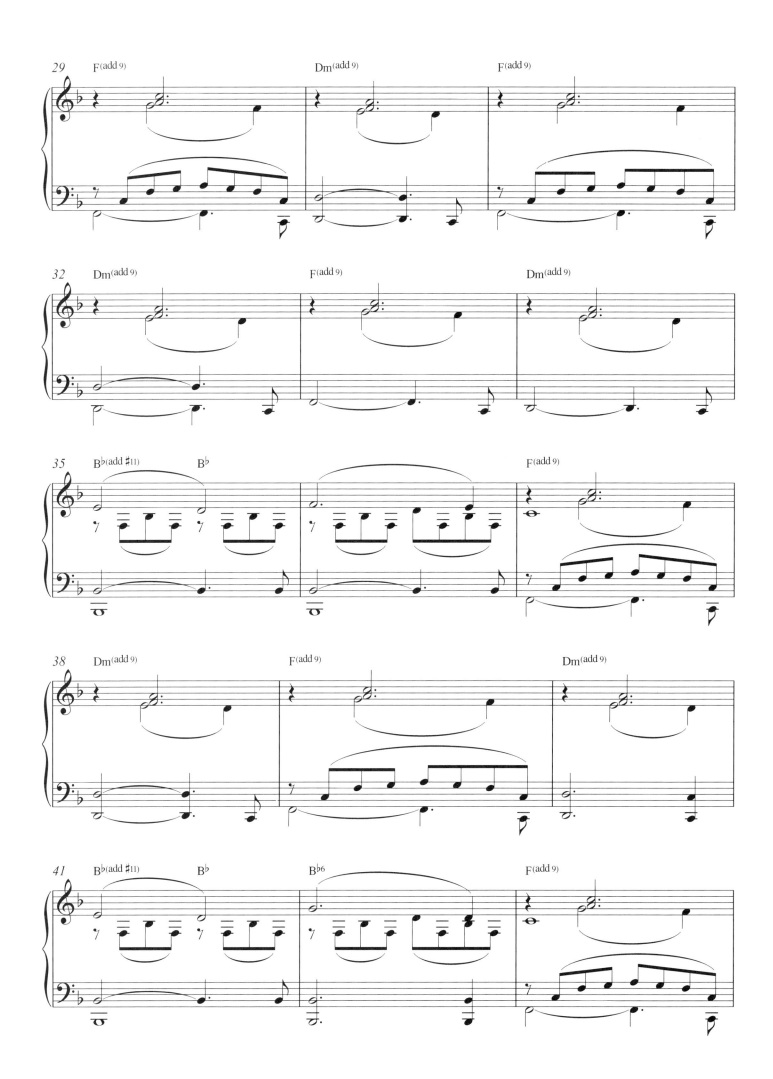

The South Bank Show

Caprice No. 24

Music by Andrew Lloyd Webber

Bringing you the words and the music

All the latest music in print... rock & pop plus jazz, blues, country, classical and the best in West End show scores.

- Books to match your favourite CDs.

- Book-and-CD titles with high quality backing tracks for you to play along to. Now you can play guitar or piano with your favourite artist... or simply sing along!

- Audition songbooks with CD backing tracks for both male and female singers for all those with stars in their eyes.

- Can't read music? No problem, you can still play all the hits with our wide range of chord songbooks.

- Check out our range of instrumental tutorial titles, taking you from novice to expert in no time at all!

- Musical show scores include *The Phantom Of The Opera*, *Les Misérables*, *Mamma Mia* and many more hit productions.

- DVD master classes featuring the techniques of top artists.